The Green Fern Zoo

Unit 4 Reader

Skills Strand

OBSOLETE

Amplify learning.

Core Knowledge®

Table of Contents

The Green Fern Zoo

Unit 4 Reader

Pausing Point (Stories for Assessment and Enrichment)

Meet Vern

My name is **Ver**n, and I have the best job! My job is to take you kids in to see the Green **Fer**n Zoo.

We will see things with wings and things with scales, things that bite and things that sting, things that creep and things that swim.

I have lots of fun facts and tales to share with you. So let's see the zoo and have some fun!

Things That Swim

I hope you kids like things that swim, be·c<u>au</u>se this is the room <u>where</u> we keep all the fish.

The fish h<u>ere</u> are trout. A trout is a fish that swims in cool lakes and creeks. You can see that they have lots of spots and marks. The spots and marks help the trout hide. They make the trout look a lot like the sand on the bed of a creek.

Here's a big fish that makes all of the wee fish run and hide. This is a reef sh**ar**k. It has that name b<u>e</u>·c<u>au</u>se it likes to make its home close to a reef, <u>where</u> there are lots of fish.

You can see that the reef shark has fins and a set of gills on its side. You can not see them from here, but this shark has lots of sharp teeth in its mouth.

Would a reef shark bite you? Well, you are not the lunch that this shark would like best. A reef shark likes to feed on squid, crabs, and shrimp. But it would be smart not to get the reef shark mad at you all the same!

Chimps

Next, let's see the chimps. We have ten chimps here at the Green Fern Zoo. You can see them all out there if you look hard.

The one you see here is Bess. She has a snack in her mouth. Bess and the rest of the chimps like to munch on plants, nuts, and seeds.

Do you see that chimp with the stick? That's **B**a**r**t. **B**a**r**t likes to have ants **for** lunch. To get the ants, he takes a stick and sticks it in an ant hill. Then he lifts it up and licks off the ants. Yum, yum!

The chimp with the rope in his hand is Max. He's just a babe. He was **bor**n in **Mar**ch. Bess is his mom.

Max is a lot of fun. He likes to swing on the rope and splash in the pool.

The two chimps up on the rocks are Carl and Norm. Carl is the one on the left. Carl and Norm are pals. But they were not pals last week.

Last week we gave them a branch from a fig tree for lunch. Norm took the branch and ran off with it. He ate all of the figs. Carl was mad at Norm all week.

But that was last week. This week the two of them are pals.

17

Mandrills

Here you can see t<u>wo</u> man·drills. Man·drills are a lot like chimps.

D<u>o</u> you like the red nose? The man·drill with the red nose is a male.

The man·drill on the left is groom·ing the male with the red nose. She is look·ing **for** ticks and bugs. Man·drills like groom·ing b<u>e</u>·c<u>au</u>se it makes them look good and feel good, too.

Look! One of the man·drills is yawn·ing! You can see that he has long, sharp teeth. Those sharp teeth help him chop up his food.

Man·drills like a lot of foods. We feed our man·drills ants, grass, nuts, **bar**k, plant shoots, and roots.

Man·drills have sacks in·side th<u>eir</u> cheeks. They can stuff food in the sacks and keep it there un·til they need a snack. Then they pop the food out and munch on it!

Things with Wings

Next, let's see s<u>o</u>m<u>e</u> things with wings.

This is a puff·in. He makes his home up n**or**th, not too f**ar** from the N**or**th Pole.

Look at those cute feet! But they are not just cute. The puff·in's feet help him swim.

Note, as well, his big bill. The puff·in can use his bill to get fish.

Puff·ins are **b**o**r**n fr<u>o</u>m eggs. The puff·in mom and dad sit on th<u>eir</u> egg. The mom sits. Then the dad sits. In the end, the chick pops out of the shell. The mom and dad take care of the chick un·til it can care **f**or it·self. Look! That puff·in has fish in h**er** bill! She will feed those fish to h**er** chick.

In this next room, we have a finch. Un·like the puff·in, the finch makes a home in wood·lands. He can use his bill to snap up grass seeds f**or** food.

I'm sad to tell you that the finch is gett·ing to be quite rare. We are proud to have five of them here at the Green F**er**n Zoo.

Big Cats

Do you like cats? If you do, look there in the grass. Do you see the cat?

That is not the **so**rt of cat that you keep in y<u>ou</u>r home and feed cat food. That is a bob·cat.

Bob·cats are good hunt·**er**s. They hunt rabb·its, rats, and s<u>o</u>me·times deer and sheep.

That bob·cat's name is Rob·**er**t, **or** Bob f**or** sh**or**t. Get it?

If you look up on that rock, you will see a cat that's bigg·**er** than a bob·cat. It's a pan·th**er**.

Pan·th**er**s can have spots. They can be tan, too. Here at the Green F**er**n Zoo, we have t<u>wo</u> black pan·th**er**s. The name of this one is Jet.

That's Jet's sis·t**er**, Flash, up on the tree branch. Flash has strong legs that help h**er** run fast. She has sh**ar**p teeth and sh**ar**p claws that help h**er** hunt rabb·its and deer. She can use h**er** claws to scam·p**er** up a tree if she needs to.

You can see that she is not all black like Jet. She has s<u>o</u>m<u>e</u> spots.

Groundhogs

Here you can see a ground·hog.

Ground·hogs have sh**arp** claws that help them dig holes in the ground. They spend a lot of time d<u>ow</u>n in those d**ar**k holes.

Ground·hogs like to feed on grass and plants. But when they run out of th__eir__ holes to get food, they have to be on the look·out. S_ome_ critt·**er**s, like bob·cats and snakes, like to dine on ground·hogs. This ground·hog here is sitt·ing up to see if there is a snake **or** a bob·cat close by.

This ground·hog is named Pepp·**er**. We f**ee**d h**er** grass, tree b**ar**k, and in·sects, but the food that she likes best is c**or**n. We found that out yes·t**er**·d_ay_ m**or**n·ing when she got out from h_o_m h**er** pen.

We found h**er** in the pett·ing zoo. She ate a lot of the c**or**n that was there f**or** the ducks and hens.

The Reptile Room

Who likes snakes? Hands up if you like them!

Some kids like snakes best of all, and some kids can't stand them. If you do not like snakes, you can skip this next room be·cause it is the rep·tile room.

This is a gar·ter snake.
Gar·ter snakes feed on slugs,
in·sects, and frogs. For those
critt·ers, the gar·ter snake is a
kill·er. But for us, it is harm·less.
A gar·ter snake could bite you,
but its bite would not make you
sick.

This is a ratt·l**er**. He is a des·**er**t dwell·**er** that hunts f**or** rats and rabb·its. He has a patt·**er**n on his scales that helps him blend in and hide in the des·**er**t sands. When the ratt·l**er** is hidd·en, it is h**ar**d f**or** rats and rabb·its to see him.

A ratt·**ler** is not h**ar**m·less like a g**ar**·**ter** snake. If you ev·**er** see this snake hiss·ing and coil·ing up, you bett·**er** stand back and let it be. The ratt·**ler** has sh**ar**p fangs, and a bite from a ratt·**ler** c<u>ou</u>ld kill you. But we are safe here in the rep·tile room. There is a sheet of glass keep·ing us safe fr<u>o</u>m the snakes.

Termites

What d<u>o</u> you kids like to have for lunch? Hot dogs? Chick·en nugg·ets?

What if I gave you a lump of wood **or** a big tree stump f**or** lunch? W<u>ou</u>ld you like that?

Well, if you were a **ter**·mite, you w<u>ou</u>ld like it. **Ter**·mites are in·sects that like to munch on wood.

See this big spike stick·ing up from the ground? It looks **sor**t of like a rock, but it is a **ter**·mite mound. If you c<u>ou</u>ld look in·side, you w<u>ou</u>ld see lots of **ter**·mites.

If you w<u>ou</u>ld like to see what **ter**·mites look like, take a peek in this box.

As you can see, **ter**·mites look a lot like ants. They have six legs like ants. A **ter**·mite mound has a queen <u>who</u> makes eggs, just like in an ant·hill. Here you can see that the **ter**·mite queen is much bigg·**er** than the rest of the **ter**·mites.

W<u>ou</u>ld a **ter**·mite munch on y<u>our</u> home? It w<u>ou</u>ld if y<u>our</u> home is made of wood. The **ter**·mites from a big mound c<u>ou</u>ld have y<u>our</u> liv·ing room f**or** lunch and y<u>our</u> bed·room f**or** dinn·**er**!

River Otters

Do you like to run and jump?
Do you like to chase your pals?
Do you like to splash in the pool
in the summ·**er**? Do you like to
slide down hills in the win·**ter**?

Well, if you like to do those
things, you would make a good
ott·**er**! You can see three of our
riv·**er** ott·**er**s up on the rocks:
Al·ex, All·en, and Ag·nes. That's
Al·ex up on top of All·en. The
last one is Ag·nes.

Ott·**er**s have sh**or**t, strong legs with webb**ed** paws and sh**ar**p claws. The webb·ing helps the ott·**er**s swim fast and get th<u>eir</u> food. Riv·**er** ott·**er**s hunt f**or** fish, frogs, and crabs.

When it is time f**or** bed, the riv·**er** ott·**er**s scam·p**er** to th<u>eir</u> den. They have nests on land that are lin**ed** with grass, moss, and b**ar**k.

Cranes and Spoon·bills

Here you can see t<u>wo</u> sand·hill cranes.

A sand·hill crane has long legs, a **dark**, point·**ed** bill, and a red spot next to its bill. Sand·hill cranes are found in wet·lands. They like to hunt **for** frogs, snakes, and in·sects.

Those are sand·hill cranes, too. In fact, that's a mom and a dad with th<u>eir</u> chicks. When sand·hill cranes mate, they tilt th<u>eir</u> bills up and make hoot·ing sounds. Then the mom and dad make a nest. The mom sits on the eggs f**or** 4 weeks un·til the chicks are b**or**n.

That's a spoon·bill. He has that name be·cause his bill is shaped like a spoon.

The spoon·bill wades in pools to get his food. He swings his bill back and forth. If he feels an in·sect swimm·ing in·side his bill, he snaps it shut.

When spoon·bills mate, they make a nest. When the chicks are born, they can't see. The mom and dad have to care for them until they can see.

The Ostrich

This is an os·trich. He is a big one. He tips the scales at close to t<u>wo</u> hun·dred pounds.

An os·trich has wings that it can flap, but it can't get off the ground. Still, an os·trich can run fast on land. It can run as fast as a **car**!

If it gets mad, an os·trich can kick you. My pal Fred here at the zoo got kick**ed** b<u>y</u> an os·trich. The os·trich broke Fred's leg in three spots! Ouch!

Deer

Look there! D<u>o</u> you see the t<u>wo</u> deer in the woods? The one <u>who</u> is look·ing at us is named Hope.

Hope was not b**or**n in this zoo. I found h**er** b<u>y</u> my home one m**or**n·ing af·t**er** a st**or**m. A tree fell on h**er** and broke h**er** leg. She c<u>ou</u>ld not stand up.

I drove h**er** here and the vet fix**ed** up h**er** leg. We nam**ed** h**er** Hope and found a spot f**or** h**er** in the zoo. To·d<u>ay</u> h**er** leg is fine and she is as strong as ev·**er**.

The Petting Zoo

Well, kids, the last thing that you all get to see is the pett·ing zoo.

You can't pet the os·trich, the ott·**er**s, **or** the spoon·bills. And it would not be wise to pet the pan·th**er or** the bob·cat! But in this p**ar**t of the zoo, you can pet all of the critt·**er**s.

This rabb·it's name is Hoss. He likes it when you rub his neck.

Here are two chick·ens. They like it when you toss them seed corn.

You can pet the chick·ens, too. But some·times they get scared. It's best if you do not run up to them be·cause runn·ing scares them.

There's Pam, our pet pig. You can pet h**er**, too. Pam likes to be pett·**ed**.

Well, kids, that's it f**or** m<u>e</u>. I hope you had a good time at the zoo to·d<u>ay</u>. I had fun point·ing out s<u>ome</u> of the critt·**er**s that I like best.

I hope s<u>ome</u> of you can vi·sit with y<u>our</u> moms and dads. There is so much to see here at the Green F**er**n Zoo. You c<u>ou</u>ld vis·it us five times and still see lots of cool things!

About this Book

This book has been created for use by students learning to read with the Core Knowledge Reading Program. Readability levels are suitable for early readers. The book has also been carefully leveled in terms of its "code load," or the number of spellings used in the stories.

The English writing system is complex. It uses more than 200 spellings to stand for 40-odd sounds. Many sounds can be spelled several different ways, and many spellings can be pronounced several different ways. This book has been designed to make early reading experiences simpler and more productive by using a subset of the available spellings. It uses *only* spellings that students have been taught to sound out as part of their phonics lessons, plus a handful of Tricky Words, which have also been deliberately introduced in the lessons. This means that the stories will be 100% decodable if they are assigned at the proper time.

As the students move through the program, they learn new spellings and the "code load" in the decodable Readers increases gradually. The code load graphic on this page indicates the number of spellings students are expected to know in order to read the first story of the book and the number of spellings students are expected to know in order to read the final stories in the book. The columns on the inside back cover list the specific spellings and Tricky Words students are expected to recognize at the beginning of this Reader. The bullets at the bottom of the inside back cover identify spellings, Tricky Words, and other topics that are introduced gradually in the unit this Reader accompanies.

Visit us on the web at www.coreknowledge.org

CORE KNOWLEDGE LANGUAGE ARTS

SERIES EDITOR-IN-CHIEF
E. D. Hirsch, Jr.

PRESIDENT
Linda Bevilacqua

EDITORIAL STAFF
Carolyn Gosse, Senior Editor - Preschool
Khara Turnbull, Materials Development Manager
Michelle L. Warner, Senior Editor - Listening & Learning

Mick Anderson
Robin Blackshire
Maggie Buchanan
Paula Coyner
Sue Fulton
Sara Hunt
Erin Kist
Robin Luecke
Rosie McCormick
Cynthia Peng
Liz Pettit
Ellen Sadler
Deborah Samley
Diane Auger Smith
Sarah Zelinke

DESIGN AND GRAPHICS STAFF
Scott Ritchie, Creative Director

Kim Berrall
Michael Donegan
Liza Greene
Matt Leech
Bridget Moriarty
Lauren Pack

CONSULTING PROJECT MANAGEMENT SERVICES
ScribeConcepts.com

ADDITIONAL CONSULTING SERVICES
Ang Blanchette
Dorrit Green
Carolyn Pinkerton

ACKNOWLEDGMENTS

These materials are the result of the work, advice, and encouragement of numerous individuals over many years. Some of those singled out here already know the depth of our gratitude; others may be surprised to find themselves thanked publicly for help they gave quietly and generously for the sake of the enterprise alone. To helpers named and unnamed we are deeply grateful.

CONTRIBUTORS TO EARLIER VERSIONS OF THESE MATERIALS

Susan B. Albaugh, Kazuko Ashizawa, Nancy Braier, Kathryn M. Cummings, Michelle De Groot, Diana Espinal, Mary E. Forbes, Michael L. Ford, Ted Hirsch, Danielle Knecht, James K. Lee, Diane Henry Leipzig, Martha G. Mack, Liana Mahoney, Isabel McLean, Steve Morrison, Juliane K. Munson, Elizabeth B. Rasmussen, Laura Tortorelli, Rachael L. Shaw, Sivan B. Sherman, Miriam E. Vidaver, Catherine S. Whittington, Jeannette A. Williams

We would like to extend special recognition to Program Directors Matthew Davis and Souzanne Wright who were instrumental to the early development of this program.

SCHOOLS

We are truly grateful to the teachers, students, and administrators of the following schools for their willingness to field test these materials and for their invaluable advice: Capitol View Elementary, Challenge Foundation Academy (IN), Community Academy Public Charter School, Lake Lure Classical Academy, Lepanto Elementary School, New Holland Core Knowledge Academy, Paramount School of Excellence, Pioneer Challenge Foundation Academy, New York City PS 26R (The Carteret School), PS 30X (Wilton School), PS 50X (Clara Barton School), PS 96Q, PS 102X (Joseph O. Loretan), PS 104Q (The Bays Water), PS 214K (Michael Friedsam), PS 223Q (Lyndon B. Johnson School), PS 308K (Clara Cardwell), PS 333Q (Goldie Maple Academy), Sequoyah Elementary School, South Shore Charter Public School, Spartanburg Charter School, Steed Elementary School, Thomas Jefferson Classical Academy, Three Oaks Elementary, West Manor Elementary.

And a special thanks to the CKLA Pilot Coordinators Anita Henderson, Yasmin Lugo-Hernandez, and Susan Smith, whose suggestions and day-to-day support to teachers using these materials in their classrooms was critical.

WRITERS

Matthew M. Davis, Core Knowledge Staff